Dear Reader,

I warn you.

Do not be deceived.

Old fairytale fables
should **not** be believed.
To trust all the tales
you have read is unwise.
The truth that I share
will completely surprise.

—Katie Pye

Start important conversations easily with the
Fairytale Fraud series.
Check out our free resources and explore more at
www.headstartthinking.com

To Malachi. You bring an insane amount of joy to my life.
I love you more than you can imagine. Love Mum

To Loretto. Love Magnus

BREAKING NEWS!

Katie Pye   Magnus Blomster

Remember poor Humpty
who sat on a wall?
He tittered and tottered
then had a great fall!
While all the king's horses
and all the king's men
tried hard to put Humpty
together again,
that wasn't the end
as you're taught to expect.
There's more to this tale
than most people suspect.

King Dumpty each year gave a 'Kingdom Address'.
His speech would be brief,

"It's a year of success!
We won't change a thing!
We are safe as we are!
It's helped us and served us
and saved us this far."

To keep things the same the town gates were shut tight,
and Eggsville repeated the same day and night.

His subjects felt glum with the daily humdrum
and Humpty, his son, bemoaned what they'd become.

"Please, Dad," he would beg, "there is more we can be!
I want to explore and to learn about me!"
His dad would look stern,
         "You are safe as you are.
         It's helped you and served you
         and saved you this far."

And so, the eggs yawned through a life that was plain.
But nearing the speech, Humpty tried once again.
King Dumpty spoke sharply, "I've said this before!
You pestering child. . .do not ask anymore!"

Poor Humpty looked shocked
and he raced off upset.

The King was stunned too and
he started to fret,

"Page, summon my men!"

His page bugled the call.

And that's when poor Humpty...

FELL DOWN OFF THE WALL!

The king was beside himself pacing around.
The king's men returned, "Humpty could not be found!"
"Then open the gates!" the king ordered his men,
"We'll open them now, but then never again."

The horses were readied. The gate creaked ajar.
Then out rode the horsemen, but not very far!
They rounded a corner and found with a fright.

A ghastly,
    a gruesome,
        a terrible sight.

The horsemen all wailed,

"**Humpty Dumpty is dead!**"

"I'm not in the least," a familiar voice said.

"In fact, I feel egg-cellent! **I feel like me!** I'm being the Humpty I wanted to be."

They all gasped with shock as the head horseman cried,

"You weren't just a shell! There was something inside!"

They picked up the shell bits and laughed with a wink,
"I wonder what King Dumpty's going to think!"

The king was astonished, relieved, and then scared,
"I'm glad you're alright, but this **can not** be shared.
We haven't much time. Summon all of my men."

"We need to put Humpty together again!"

Poor Humpty protested, "I want to be me!"
The king snapped back, angry,
"You really don't see?
We can't change a thing!
We are safe as we are!
It's helped us and served us
and saved us this far!"

But secrets like this are great trouble to hide,
and soon Humpty's fall was **big gossip** outside.

The clock ticked away while the king paced and paced.
Poor Humpty lay still while the king's men all raced.

But try as they might, the exhausted king's men

just couldn't put Humpty together again.

They heard the bell ring for the speech to take place.
King Dumpty and Humpty raced upstairs at pace.

The king stepped ahead to address the town square,
then gasped at a change he could never repair.

For **speckled**,  or **spotted**,

or **striped**, or **just plain**;

coloured, or **dashed**,

no one looked just the same.

All of the Eggs had come out of their shell!
King Dumpty swooned, then he fainted and fell.

Alarmed, Humpty peeked and then gaped at the sight.
The birds were all waiting. He swallowed with fright.

"It's clear," he addressed them,
""there's more we can be.

It's time to explore
and to learn and be free."

The crowd clapped and cheered, then he smiled with surprise.
His dad, now recovered, was wiping his eyes.

"Things won't be the same," he agreed, "that is true!
We'll welcome this change, and we'll start here with you!"

The crowd roared applause as the father and son
removed Humpty's shell 'til the job was quite done!
They cheered even louder to hear their king state,

"and now, lovely Eggsville, let's open the gate!"

HOORAY!   YIPPIE!   YAY!

YES!   AWESOME!

New Eggsville was vibrant and life-filled and fun
as everyone relished who they had become.

As King Dumpty watched and admired and learned,
he slowly, in time, also hankered and yearned.

'Til one day, when Humpty
    perched up on his wall,
        he heard a familiar but jubilant call. . .

"Hey Humpty," a voice sang,

"just look at me flit!
I took off a bit...
and I just couldn't quit!"

"I've watched how you've changed and I've learned it's okay!
I talked to my worries to keep them at bay.
It's scary, but stuck in the same is a bore.
Now race time!" he laughed, "it is time to explore!"

BEHIND THE SCENES

Have you ever wanted a change you couldn't make happen?
Is there something you would like to change now?

What helped me cope with my change?
What might help you with your changes?

What do you think is the best thing about change? What is the worst?

ACT ON IT!

- Practice a change!
  Name something small you can change and change it this week!

- Have a special 'goodbye' to farewell what you had.

FACING A CHANGE? WHICH OF THESE MIGHT HELP?

Make time for 'normal' and fun stuff!

List off things that will stay the same and things that will change.

Try and work out what you are feeling and why? Drawing it might help.

Find new opportunities. Flying races?

Remind yourself of changes you've coped with before. Tell yourself you'll be okay!

Ask as many questions as you need...or for help!

MEMORY MOTTOS

Everyone faces change, and everyone copes with it differently. That's ok. Remember these helpful questions when you are facing a change:

What am I free to choose right now? You still have power!

What really matters? Sometimes a little perspective helps!

What superpowers do I have to help me through this?

Access more 'Behind the Scenes' materials free on
www.headstartthinking.com

MORE FAIRYTALE FRAUD EXPOSED

Create even more conversations with your children with our growing Fairytale Fraud series.

Check out **www.headstartthinking.com** for the range of topics, as well as free resources.

Create conversations about:

Gratitude

Trip Trap Trouble
(Billy Goats Gruff)

Managing Conflict

The Witch's Mix-Up
(Hansel and Gretel)

Healthy Habits

Ready for Rescue?
(Rapunzel)

Learning from Others

Put Some Pants On!
(The Emperor's New Clothes)

Healthy Grief / Social Media

The Lost Years
(Sleeping Beauty)